www.EffortlessMath.com

... So Much More Online!

✓ FREE Math lessons

✓ More Math learning books!

✓ Mathematics Worksheets

✓ Online Math Tutors

Need a PDF version of this book?

Please visit www.EffortlessMath.com

5 Full Length ALEKS Math Practice Tests

The Practice You Need to Ace the ALEKS Math Test

By

Reza Nazari & Ava Ross

Copyright © 2019

Reza Nazari & Ava Ross

All inquiries should be addressed to:

info@effortlessMath.com

www.EffortlessMath.com

ISBN-13: 978-1-64612-109-0

ISBN-10: 1-64612-109-0

Published by: Effortless Math Education

www.EffortlessMath.com

Description

5 Full-Length ALEKS Math Practice Tests, which reflects the 2019 and 2020 test guidelines and topics, is designed to help you hone your math skills, overcome your exam anxiety, and boost your confidence -- and do your best to ace the ALEKS Math Test. The realistic and full-length ALEKS Math tests show you how the test is structured and what math topics you need to master. The practice test questions are followed by answer explanations to help you find your weak areas, learn from your mistakes, and raise your ALEKS Math score.

The surest way to succeed on ALEKS Math Test is with intensive practice in every math topic tested-- and that's what you will get in *5 Full-Length ALEKS Math Practice Tests*. This ALEKS Math new edition has been updated to replicate questions appearing on the most recent ALEKS Math tests. This is a precious learning tool for ALEKS Math test takers who need extra practice in math to improve their ALEKS Math score. After taking the ALEKS Math practice tests in this book, you will have solid foundation and adequate practice that is necessary to succeed on the ALEKS Math test. **This book is your ticket to ace the ALEKS Math!**

5 Full-Length ALEKS Math Practice Tests contains many exciting and unique features to help you improve your test scores, including:

- Content 100% aligned with the 2019 - 2020 ALEKS test

- Written by ALEKS Math tutors and test experts

- Complete coverage of all ALEKS Math concepts and topics which you will be tested

- Detailed answers and explanations for every ALEKS Math practice questions to help you learn from your mistakes

- 5 full-length practice tests (featuring new question types) with detailed answers

This ALEKS Math book and other Effortless Math Education books are used by thousands of students each year to help them review core content areas, brush-up in math, discover their strengths and weaknesses, and achieve their best scores on the ALEKS test.

About the Author

Reza Nazari is the author of more than 100 Math learning books including:
– **Math and Critical Thinking Challenges:** For the Middle and High School Student
– **ALEKS Math in 30 Days**
– **ASVAB Math Workbook 2018 - 2019**
– **Effortless Math Education Workbooks**
– **and many more Mathematics books ...**

Reza is also an experienced Math instructor and a test–prep expert who has been tutoring students since 2008. Reza is the founder of Effortless Math Education, a tutoring company that has helped many students raise their standardized test scores—and attend the colleges of their dreams. Reza provides an individualized custom learning plan and the personalized attention that makes a difference in how students view math.

You can contact Reza via email at:
reza@EffortlessMath.com

Find Reza's professional profile at:
goo.gl/zoC9rJ

Contents

Time to Test

Time to refine your skill with a practice examination

Take a REAL ALEKS Mathematics test to simulate the test day experience. After you've finished, score your test using the answers and explanations section.

Before You Start

- You'll need a pencil and scratch papers to take the test.

- For these practice tests, don't time yourself. Spend time as much as you need.

- After you've finished the test, review the answer key to see where you went wrong.

Good Luck!

ALEKS Mathematics Practice Test 1

2019 - 2020

Total number of questions: 30

Total time (Calculator): No time limit

Calculators are permitted for ALEKS Math Test.

1) How many tiles of $8\ cm^2$ is needed to cover a floor of dimension $7\ cm$ by $24\ cm$?

2) What is the area of a square whose diagonal is $6\ cm$?

3) What is the value of x in the following figure?

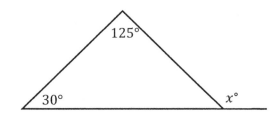

4) What is the value of y in the following system of equation?
$$3x - 4y = -20$$
$$-x + 2y = 20$$

5) How long does a 420–miles trip take moving at 65 miles per hour (mph)?

6) When 50% of 60 is added to 12% of 600, the resulting number is:

7) What is the solution of the following inequality?
$$|x - 10| \leq 4$$

8) A bag contains 18 balls: two green, five black, eight blue, a brown, a red and one white. If 17 balls are removed from the bag at random, what is the probability that a brown ball has been removed?

9) If a tree casts a 22–foot shadow at the same time that a 3 feet yardstick casts a 2–foot shadow, what is the height of the tree?

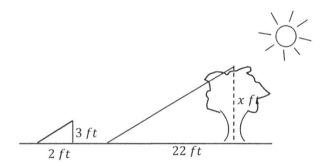

10) What is the value of $cos\ 30°$?

11) Simplify.

$$2x^2 + 4y^5 - x^2 + 2z^3 - 2y^2 + 2x^3 - 2y^5 + 6z^3$$

12) In five successive hours, a car traveled $40\ km, 45\ km, 50\ km, 35\ km$ and $55\ km$. In the next five hours, it traveled with an average speed of $65\ km\ per\ hour$. Find the total distance the car traveled in 10 hours.

13) From last year, the price of gasoline has increased from $1.40 per gallon to $1.75 per gallon. The new price is what percent of the original price?

14) 6 liters of water are poured into an aquarium that's $25cm$ long, $5cm$ wide, and $60cm$ high. How many cm will the water level in the aquarium rise due to this added water? ($1\ liter\ of\ water = 1,000\ cm^3$)

15) If a box contains red and blue balls in ratio of $2:3$, how many red balls are there if 75 blue balls are in the box?

16) A chemical solution contains 6% alcohol. If there is $24\ ml$ of alcohol, what is the volume of the solution?

17) If $\frac{5x}{16} = \frac{x-1}{4}$, $x =$

18) Simplify $(-4 + 9i)(3 + 5i)$,

19) If $\tan\theta = \frac{5}{12}$ and $\sin\theta > 0$, then $\cos\theta = ?$

20) If 60% of x equal to 30% of 20, then what is the value of $(x + 7)^2$?

21) A boat sails 80 miles south and then 60 miles east. How far is the boat from its start point?

22) If $x \begin{bmatrix} 2 & 0 \\ 0 & 4 \end{bmatrix} = \begin{bmatrix} x + 3y - 5 & 0 \\ 0 & 2y + 10 \end{bmatrix}$, what is the product of x and y?

23) A number is chosen at random from 1 to 20. Find the probability of not selecting a composite number.

24) Removing which of the following numbers will change the average of the numbers to 8?
$$1, 4, 5, 8, 11, 12$$

25) If $y = 4ab + 3b^3$, what is y when $a = 2$ and $b = 4$?

26) If $f(x) = 6 + x$ and $g(x) = -x^2 - 1 - 2x$, then find $(g - f)(x)$.

27) If cotangent of an angel β is 2, then the tangent of angle β is ...

28) When point $A\ (11, 4)$ is reflected over the $y-$axis to get the point B, what are the coordinates of point B?

29) If the area of trapezoid is 100, what is the perimeter of the trapezoid?

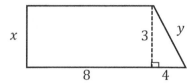

30) If $f(x) = 2x^3 + 5x^2 + 2x$ and $g(x) = -3$, what is the value of $f(g(x))$?

This is the end of Practice Test 1.

ALEKS Mathematics Practice Test 2

2019 - 2020

Total number of questions: 30

Total time (Calculator): No time limit

Calculators are permitted for ALEKS Math Test.

1) If $f(x) = 4x - 2$ and $g(x) = x^2 - x$, then find $(\frac{f}{g})(x)$.

2) A bank is offering 4.5% simple interest on a savings account. If you deposit $12,000, how much interest will you earn in two years?

3) If the ratio of home fans to visiting fans in a crowd is $3:2$ and all 24,000 seats in a stadium are filled, how many visiting fans are in attendance?

4) If the interior angles of a quadrilateral are in the ratio $2:3:3:4$, what is the measure of the largest angle?

5) If the area of a circle is 49 square meters, what is its diameter?

6) The length of a rectangle is $\frac{5}{4}$ times its width. If the width is 20, what is the perimeter of this rectangle?

7) In the figure below, line A is parallel to line B. What is the value of angle x?

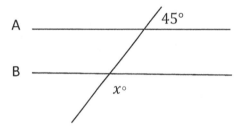

8) An angle is equal to one ninth of its supplement. What is the measure of that angle?

9) What is the value of y in the following system of equations?
$$2x + 5y = 11$$
$$4x - 2y = -14$$

10) Last week 25,000 fans attended a football match. This week three times as many bought tickets, but one sixth of them cancelled their tickets. How many are attending this week?

11) If $sin\ A = \frac{1}{3}$ in a right triangle and the angle A is an acute angle, then what is $cos\ A$?

12) In the standard (x, y) coordinate system plane, what is the area of the circle with the following equation?
$$(x + 2)^2 + (y - 4)^2 = 25$$

13) Convert 580,000 to scientific notation.

14) The ratio of boys to girls in a school is $2:3$. If there are 500 students in a school, how many boys are in the school.

15) If 150% of a number is 75, then what is 80% of that number?

16) If $A = \begin{bmatrix} -1 & 2 \\ 1 & -2 \end{bmatrix}$ and $B = \begin{bmatrix} 3 & 1 \\ -2 & 3 \end{bmatrix}$, then $2A - B =$

17) What is the solution of the following inequality?

$$|x - 2| \geq 4$$

18) If $\tan x = \frac{8}{15}$, then $\sin x =$

19) $(x^6)^{\frac{7}{8}}$ equal to?

20) What are the zeroes of the function $f(x) = x^3 + 5x^2 + 6x$?

21) If $x + sin^2a + cos^2a = 3$, then x = ?

22) If $\sqrt{5x} = \sqrt{y}$, then $x =$

23) The average weight of 18 girls in a class is 55 kg and the average weight of 32 boys in the same class is 62 kg. What is the average weight of all the 50 students in that class?

24) What is the value of the expression $5(x - 2y) + (2 - x)^2$ when $x = 3$ and $y = -3$?

25) Sophia purchased a sofa for $530.40. The sofa is regularly priced at $631. What was the percent discount Sophia received on the sofa?

26) If one angle of a right triangle measures 60°, what is the sine of the other acute angle?

27) Simplify $\frac{4-3i}{-4i}$?

28) The average of five consecutive numbers is 40. What is the smallest number?

29) What is the slope of a line that is perpendicular to the line
$$4x - 2y = 14?$$

30) If $f(x) = 2x^3 + 4$ and $(x) = \frac{1}{x}$, what is the value of $f(g(x))$?

This is the end of Practice Test 2.

ALEKS Mathematics Practice Test 3

2019 - 2020

Total number of questions: 30

Total time (Calculator): No time limit

Calculators are permitted for ALEKS Math Test.

(On a real ALEKS test, there is an onscreen calculator to use.)

1) How many tiles of $8\ cm^2$ is needed to cover a floor of dimension $6\ cm$ by $24\ cm$?

2) What is the area of a square whose diagonal is $8\ cm$?

3) What is the value of x in the following figure?

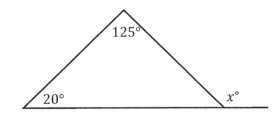

4) What is the value of y in the following system of equation?
$$3x - 4y = -20$$
$$-x + 2y = 10$$

5) How long does a 420–miles trip take moving at 50 miles per hour (mph)?

6) When 40% of 60 is added to 12% of 600, the resulting number is:

7) What is the solution of the following inequality?
$$|x - 10| \leq 3$$

8) In the following figure, ABCD is a rectangle, and E and F are points on AD and DC, respectively. The area of ΔBED is 16, and the area of ΔBDF is 18. What is the perimeter of the rectangle?

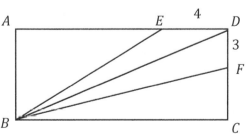

9) If a tree casts a 24–foot shadow at the same time that a 3 feet yardstick casts a 2–foot shadow, what is the height of the tree?

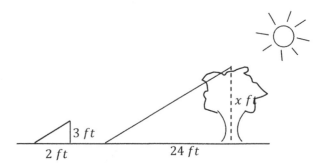

10) A ladder leans against a wall forming a $60°$ angle between the ground and the ladder. If the bottom of the ladder is 30 feet away from the wall, how long is the ladder?

11) Simplify.

$$2x^2 + 3y^5 - x^2 + 2z^3 - 2y^2 + 2x^3 - 2y^5 + 5z^3$$

12) In five successive hours, a car traveled $40\ km, 45\ km, 50\ km, 35\ km$ and $55\ km$. In the next five hours, it traveled with an average speed of $50\ km\ per\ hour$. Find the total distance the car traveled in 10 hours.

13) In the following figure, ABCD is a rectangle. If $a = \sqrt{3}$, and $b = 2a$, find the area of the shaded region. (the shaded region is a trapezoid)

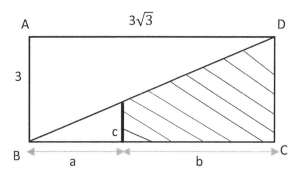

14) 6 liters of water are poured into an aquarium that's $15cm$ long, $5cm$ wide, and $90cm$ high. How many centimeters will the water level in the aquarium rise due to this added water? ($1 \; liter \; of \; water = 1,000 \; cm^3$)

15) If a box contains red and blue balls in ratio of $2:3$, how many red balls are there if 90 blue balls are in the box?

16) A chemical solution contains 4% alcohol. If there is $24\ ml$ of alcohol, what is the volume of the solution?

17) If $\frac{3x}{16} = \frac{x-1}{4}$, $x =$

18) Simplify $(-5 + 9i)(3 + 5i)$.

19) If θ is an acute angle and $sin\ \theta = \frac{4}{5}$ then $cos\ \theta =$

20) If 60% of x equal to 30% of 20, then what is the value of $(x + 5)^2$?

21) A boat sails 40 miles south and then 30 miles east. How far is the boat from its start point?

22) What is the value of x in the following equation? $log_4(x + 2) - log_4(x - 2) = 1$

23) A number is chosen at random from 1 to 25. Find the probability of not selecting a composite number.

24) Find AC in the following triangle. Round answers to the nearest tenth.

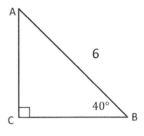

25) If $y = 4ab + 3b^3$, what is y when $a = 2$ and $b = 3$?

26) If $f(x) = 5 + x$ and $g(x) = -x^2 - 1 - 2x$, then find $(g - f)(x)$.

27) If cotangent of an angel β is 1, then the tangent of angle β is ...

28) When point $A\,(10,3)$ is reflected over the $y-$axis to get the point B, what are the coordinates of point B?

29) What is the average of circumference of figure A and area of figure B? ($\pi = 3$)

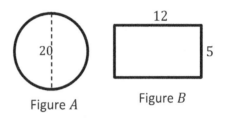

Figure A Figure B

30) If $f(x) = 2x^3 + 5x^2 + 2x$ and $g(x) = -2$, what is the value of $f(g(x))$?

This is the end of Practice Test 3.

ALEKS Mathematics Practice Test 4

2019 - 2020

Total number of questions: 30

Total time (Calculator): No time limit

Calculators are permitted for ALEKS Math Test.

(On a real ALEKS test. there is an onscreen calculator to use.)

1) If $f(x) = 3x - 1$ and $g(x) = x^2 - x$, then find $\left(\frac{f}{g}\right)(x)$.

2) A bank is offering 3.5% simple interest on a savings account. If you deposit $12,000, how much interest will you earn in two years?

3) If the ratio of home fans to visiting fans in a crowd is $3:2$ and all 25,000 seats in a stadium are filled, how many visiting fans are in attendance?

4) If the interior angles of a quadrilateral are in the ratio $1:2:3:4$, what is the measure of the largest angle?

5) If the area of a circle is 64 square meters, what is its diameter?

6) The length of a rectangle is $\frac{5}{4}$ times its width. If the width is 16, what is the perimeter of this rectangle?

7) In the figure below, line A is parallel to line B. What is the value of angle x?

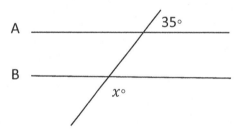

8) An angle is equal to one fifth of its supplement. What is the measure of that angle?

9) What is the value of x in the following system of equations?
$$2x + 5y = 11$$
$$4x - 2y = -14$$

10) Last week 24,000 fans attended a football match. This week three times as many bought tickets, but one sixth of them cancelled their tickets. How many are attending this week?

11) If $sin\ A = \frac{1}{4}$ in a right triangle and the angle A is an acute angle, then what is $cos\ A$?

12) In the standard (x, y) coordinate system plane, what is the area of the circle with the following equation?
$$(x + 2)^2 + (y - 4)^2 = 16$$

13) Convert 670,000 to scientific notation.

14) The ratio of boys to girls in a school is $2:3$. If there are 600 students in a school, how many boys are in the school.

15) If 150% of a number is 75, then what is 90% of that number?

16) If $A = \begin{bmatrix} -1 & 2 \\ 1 & -2 \end{bmatrix}$ and $B = \begin{bmatrix} 4 & 1 \\ -2 & 3 \end{bmatrix}$, then $2A - B =$

17) What is the solution of the following inequality?
$$|x - 2| \geq 3$$

18) If $\tan x = \frac{8}{15}$, then $\sin x =$

19) $\left(x^6\right)^{\frac{5}{8}}$ equal to?

20) What are the zeroes of the function $f(x) = x^3 + 6x^2 + 8x$?

21) If $x + \sin^2 a + \cos^2 a = 3$, then x = ?

22) If $\sqrt{6x} = \sqrt{y}$, then $x =$

23) The average weight of 18 girls in a class is $60 \; kg$ and the average weight of 32 boys in the same class is $62 \; kg$. What is the average weight of all the 50 students in that class?

24) What is the value of the expression $5(x - 2y) + (2 - x)^2$ when $x = 3$ and $y = -2$?

25) Sophia purchased a sofa for $530.40. The sofa is regularly priced at $624. What was the percent discount Sophia received on the sofa?

26) If one angle of a right triangle measures 60°, what is the sine of the other acute angle?

27) Simplify $\dfrac{5-3i}{-5i}$?

28) The average of five consecutive numbers is 38. What is the smallest number?

29) What is the slope of a line that is perpendicular to the line
$$4x - 2y = 12?$$

30) If $f(x) = 2x^4 + 2$ and $(x) = \frac{1}{x}$, what is the value of $f(g(x))$?

This is the end of Practice Test 4.

ALEKS Mathematics Practice Test 5

2019 - 2020

Total number of questions: 30

Total time (Calculator): No time limit

Calculators are permitted for ALEKS Math Test.

(On a real ALEKS test, there is an onscreen calculator to use.)

1) $(x - 5)(x^2 + 5x + 4) = ?$

2) $5 + 8 \times (-3) - [4 + 22 \times 5] \div 6 = ?$

3) Simplify. $\dfrac{\dfrac{1}{2} - \dfrac{x + 5}{4}}{\dfrac{x^2}{2} - \dfrac{5}{2}}$

4) How many 4×2 squares can fit inside a rectangle with a height of 52 and width of 12?

5) If $5 + 2x \leq 15$, what is the value of $x \leq$?

6) A man owed $4,265 on his car. After making 55 payments of $66 each, how much did he have left to pay?

7) $\left(x^4\right)^{\frac{5}{8}} =$

8) What is 2531.58245 rounded to the nearest tenth?

9) 25 is what percent of 75?

10) Last Friday Jacob had $34.52. Over the weekend he received some money for cleaning the attic. He now has $44. How much money did he receive?

11) In the following triangle what is the value of x?

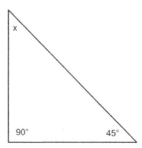

12) Find the factors of $x^2 - 7x + 12$.

13) A ladder leans against a wall forming a 60° angle between the ground and the ladder. If the bottom of the ladder is 30 feet away from the wall, how long is the ladder?

14) What is the distance between the points $(1, 3)$ and $(-2, 7)$?

15) Write the $\frac{2}{140}$ as a decimal. (round your answer to the nearest ten thousandths)

16) Liam's average (arithmetic mean) on two mathematics tests is 9. What should Liam's score be on the next test to have an overall of 10 for all the tests?

17) Find all values of x in this equation: $4x^2 + 14x + 6 = 0$

18) What is the value of x in this equation? $7^5 \times 7^8 = 7^x$

19) If a vehicle is driven 33 miles on Monday, 36 miles on Tuesday, and 30 miles on Wednesday, what is the average number of miles driven each day?

20) Find the solutions of the following equation.

$$x^2 + 2x - 5 = 0$$

21) What is the solution of the following system of equations?

$$\begin{cases} -2x - y = -9 \\ \quad 5x - 2y = 9 \end{cases}$$

22) Solve.

$$|9 - (12 \div |2 - 6|)| = ?$$

23) If $\log_2 x = 5$, then $x = ?$

24) What's the reciprocal of $\dfrac{x^3}{14}$?

25) What is the equivalent temperature of $140°F$ in Celsius?

$$C = \frac{5}{9}(F - 32)$$

26) Simplify $(-3 + 9i)(3 + 5i)$.

27) Find $tan\ \frac{2\pi}{3}$

28) If $f(x) = 5x - 1$ and $g(x) = x^2 - x$, then find $(\frac{f}{g})(x)$.

29) What is the center and radius of a circle with the following equation?

$$(x - 4)^2 + (y + 7)^2 = 3$$

30) If the center of a circle is at the point $(-4, 2)$ and its circumference equals to 2π, what is the standard form equation of the circle?

This is the end of Practice Test 5.

ALEKS Mathematics Practice Tests Answers and Explanations

Now, it's time to review your results to see where you went wrong and what areas you need to improve!

ALEKS Mathematics Practice Test 1

1) The answer is 21

The area of the floor is: $7\ cm\ \times 24\ cm = 168\ cm^2$. The number is tiles needed $=$

$$168 \div 8 = \ 21$$

2) The answer is 18

The diagonal of the square is 6. Let x be the side.

Use Pythagorean Theorem: $a^2 + \ b^2 = c^2$

$x^2 + x^2 = 6^2 \Rightarrow 2x^2 = 6^2 \Rightarrow 2x^2 = 36 \Rightarrow x^2 = 18 \Rightarrow x = \sqrt{18}$

The area of the square is: $\sqrt{18} \times \sqrt{18} = 18$

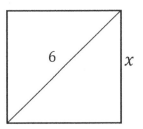

3) The answer is 155

$x = 30 + 125 = 155$

4) The answer is 20

Solve the system of equations by elimination method.

$3x - 4y = -20$
$-x + 2y = 20$ Multiply the second equation by 3, then add it to the first equation.

$\begin{array}{c} 3x \quad 4y = \quad 20 \\ 3(-x + 2y = 20) \end{array} \Rightarrow \begin{array}{c} 3x \quad 4y - \quad 20 \\ -3x + 6y = 60) \end{array} \Rightarrow$ add the equations $2y = 40 \Rightarrow y = 20$

5) The answer is 6.4 hours

Use distance formula: $Distance = Rate \times time \ \Rightarrow \ 420 = 65 \times T$, divide both sides by

$65. 420 \div 65 = T \Rightarrow T = 6.4\ hours.$ Change hours to minutes for the decimal part. $0.4\ hours = 0.4 \times 60 = 24\ minutes.$

6) The answer is 102

50% of 60 equals to: $0.50 \times 60 = 30$, 12% of 600 equals to: $0.12 \times 600 = 72$

50% of 60 is added to 12% of 600: $30 + 72 = 102$

7) **The answer is** $6 \leq x \leq 14$
   $|x - 10| \leq 4 \rightarrow -4 \leq x - 10 \leq 4 \rightarrow -4 + 10 \leq x - 10 + 10 \leq 4 + 10 \rightarrow 6 \leq x \leq 14$

8) **The answer is** $\frac{17}{18}$

If 17 balls are removed from the bag at random, there will be one ball in the bag. The probability of choosing a brown ball is 1 out of 18. Therefore, the probability of not choosing a brown ball is 17 out of 18 (or $\frac{17}{18}$) and the probability of having not a brown ball after removing 11 balls is the same.

9) **The answer is** $33\ ft$

Write a proportion and solve for x. $\frac{3}{2} = \frac{x}{22} \Rightarrow 2x = 3 \times 22 \Rightarrow x = 33\ ft$

10) **The answer is** $\frac{\sqrt{3}}{2}$

$$cos\ 30° = \frac{\sqrt{3}}{2}$$

11) **The answer is** $2y^5 + 2x^3 + 8z^3 + x^2 - 2y^2$

$$2x^2 + 4y^5 - x^2 + 2z^3 - 2y^2 + 2x^3 - 2y^5 + 6z^3$$
$$= 2x^2 - x^2 + 2x^3 - 2y^2 + 4y^5 - 2y^5 + 2z^3 + 6z^3$$
$$= x^2 + 2x^3 - 2y^2 + 2y^5 + 8z^3 = 2y^5 + 2x^3 + 8z^3 + x^2 - 2y^2$$

12) **The answer is** 550

Add the first 5 numbers. $40 + 45 + 50 + 35 + 55 = 225$, To find the distance traveled in the next 5 hours, multiply the average by number of hours.

$Distance = Average \times Rate = 65 \times 5 = 325.$ Add both numbers. $325 + 225 = 550$

13) **The answer is** 125%

The question is this: 1.75 is what percent of 1.40? Use percent formula: $part = \frac{percent}{100} \times whole$,
$1.75 = \frac{percent}{100} \times 1.40 \Rightarrow 1.75 = \frac{percent \times 1.40}{100} \Rightarrow 175 = percent \times 1.40 \Rightarrow percent = \frac{175}{1.40} = 125$

14) **The answer is** $48cm$

$One\ liter = 1,000\ cm^3 \rightarrow 6\ liters = 6,000\ cm^3$ $6,000 = 25 \times 5 \times h \rightarrow h = \frac{6,000}{125} = 48\ cm$

15) **The answer is** 50

$$\frac{2}{3} \times 75 = 50$$

16) The answer is $400 \, ml$

6% of the volume of the solution is alcohol. Let x be the volume of the solution.

Then: $6\% \; of \; x = 24 \, ml \Rightarrow 0.06 \, x = 24 \Rightarrow x = 24 \div 0.06 = 400$

17) The answer is -4

Solve for x. $\frac{5x}{16} = \frac{x-1}{4}$. Multiply the second fraction by 4. $\frac{5x}{16} = \frac{4(x-1)}{4 \times 4}$. Tow denominators are equal. Therefore, the numerators must be equal. $5x = 4x - 4, \quad 5x - 4x = -4 \qquad -4 = x$

18) The answer is $-57 + 7i$

We know that: $i = \sqrt{-1} \Rightarrow i^2 = -1$

$(-4 + 9i)(3 + 5i) = -12 - 20i + 27i + 45i^2 = -12 + 7i - 45 = -57 + 7i$

19) The answer is $\frac{12}{13}$

$tan\theta = \frac{\text{opposite}}{\text{adjacent}}, \; tan\theta = \frac{5}{12} \Rightarrow$ we have the following right triangle. Then

$c = \sqrt{5^2 + 12^2} = \sqrt{25 + 144} = \sqrt{169} = 13$

$cos\theta = \dfrac{adjacent}{hypotenuse} = \dfrac{12}{13}$

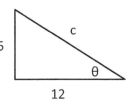

20) The answer is 289

$0.6x = (0.3) \times 20 \rightarrow x = 10 \rightarrow (x + 7)^2 = (17)^2 = 289$

21) The answer is 100 miles

Use the information provided in the question to draw the shape.

Use Pythagorean Theorem: $a^2 + b^2 = c^2$

$60^2 + 80^2 = c^2 \Rightarrow 3,600 + 6,400 = c^2 \Rightarrow 10,000 = c^2 \Rightarrow c = 100$

22) The answer is 12

Based on corresponding members from two matrices, we get: $\begin{cases} 2x = x + 3y - 5 \\ 4x = 2y + 10 \end{cases} \rightarrow$

$\begin{cases} x - 3y = -5 \\ 4x - 2y = 10 \end{cases}$, Multiply first equation by -4.

$\begin{cases} -4x + 12y = 20 \\ 4x - 2y = 10 \end{cases} \rightarrow$ add two equations. $10y = 30 \rightarrow y = 3 \rightarrow x = 4 \rightarrow x \times y = 12$

23) The answer is $\frac{9}{20}$

Set of number that are not composite between 1 and 20: $A = \{1, 2, 3, 5, 7, 11, 13, 17, 19\}$

$$Probability = \frac{number\ of\ desired\ outcomes}{number\ of\ total\ outcomes} = \frac{9}{20}$$

24) The answer is 1

Let's remove each number and calculate the average.

Remove 1. Then: $average = \frac{4+5+8+11+12}{5} = \frac{40}{5} = 8$

Remove 4. Then: $average = \frac{1+5+8+11+12}{5} = \frac{37}{5} = 7.4$

Remove 5. Then: $average = \frac{1+4+8+11+12}{5} = \frac{36}{5} = 7.2$

Remove 8. Then: $average = \frac{1+4+5+11+12}{5} = \frac{33}{5} = 6.6$

Remove 11. Then: $average = \frac{1+4+5+8+12}{5} = \frac{30}{5} = 6$

Remove 12. Then: $average = \frac{1+4+5+8+11}{5} = \frac{29}{5} = 5.8$

25) The answer is 224

$y = 4ab + 3b^3$. Plug in the values of a and b in the equation: $a = 2$ and $b = 4$

$y = 4\,(2)(4) + 3\,(4)^3 = 32\ + 3(64) = 32 + 192 = 224$

26) The answer is $- x^2 - 3x - 7$

$(g - f)(x) =\ g(x) - f(x) = (-x^2 - 1 - 2x) - (6\ +\ x)$

$- x^2 - 1 - 2x - 6 - x\ =\ - x^2 - 3x - 7$

27) The answer is 0.5

$$tangent\ \beta = \frac{1}{cotangent\ \beta} = \frac{1}{2} = 0.5$$

28) The answer is $(-11, 4)$

When points are reflected over $y-$axis, the value of y in the coordinates doesn't change and the sign of x changes. Therefore, the coordinates of point B is $(-11, 4)$.

29) The answer is 35

The area of trapezoid is: $\left(\frac{8+12}{2}\right) \times x = 100 \rightarrow 10x = 100 \rightarrow x = 10$

$y = \sqrt{3^2 + 4^2} = 5,$ Perimeter is: $12 + 10 + 8 + 5 = 35$

30) The answer is -15

$g(x) = -3$, then $f\big(g(x)\big) = f(-3) = 2\,(-3)^3 + 5(-3)^2 + 2(-3) = -54 + 45 - 6 = -15$

ALEKS Mathematics Practice Test 2

1) The answer is $\frac{4x-2}{x^2-x}$

$$\left(\frac{f}{g}\right)(x) = \frac{f(x)}{g(x)} = \frac{4x-2}{x^2-x}$$

2) The answer is $1,080$

Use simple interest formula: $I = prt$ (I = interest, p = principal, r = rate, t = time)

$$I = (12,000)(0.045)(2) = 1,080$$

3) The answer is $9,600$

Number of visiting fans: $\frac{2 \times 24,000}{5} = 9,600$

4) The answer is $120°$

The sum of all angles in a quadrilateral is 360 degrees. Let x be the smallest angle in the quadrilateral. Then the angles are: $2x, 3x, 3x, 4x$, $2x + 3x + 3x + 4x = 360 \rightarrow 12x = 360 \rightarrow x = 30$, The angles in the quadrilateral are: $60°, 90°, 90°$, and $120°$

5) The answer is $\frac{7\sqrt{\pi}}{\pi}$

Formula for the area of a circle is: $A = \pi r^2$, Using 49 for the area of the circle we have: $49 = \pi r^2$, Let's solve for the radius (r). $\frac{49}{\pi} = r^2 \rightarrow r = \sqrt{\frac{49}{\pi}} = \frac{7}{\sqrt{\pi}} = \frac{7}{\sqrt{\pi}} \times \frac{\sqrt{\pi}}{\sqrt{\pi}} = \frac{7\sqrt{\pi}}{\pi}$

6) The answer is 90
Length of the rectangle is: $\frac{5}{4} \times 20 = 25$, perimeter of rectangle is: $2 \times (20 + 25) = 90$
7) The answer is $135°$

The angle x and 45 are complementary angles. Therefore: $x + 45 = 180 \rightarrow x = 180° - 45° - 135°$

8) The answer is 18
The sum of supplement angles is 180. Let x be that angle. Therefore, $x + 9x = 180$
$10x = 180$, divide both sides by 10: $x = 18$
9) The answer is 3

Solving Systems of Equations by Elimination: Multiply the first equation by (-2), then add it to the second equation.

$$\begin{matrix} -2(2x + 5y = 11) \\ 4x - 2y = -14 \end{matrix} \Rightarrow \begin{matrix} -4x - 10y = -22 \\ 4x - 2y = -14 \end{matrix} \Rightarrow -12y = -36 \Rightarrow y = 3$$

10) The answer is 62, 500

Three times of 25,000 is 75,000. One sixth of them cancelled their tickets. One sixth of 75,000 equals 12,500 ($\frac{1}{6} \times 72,000 = 12,500$). 62,500 ($72,000 - 12,000 = 62,500$) fans are attending this week.

11) The answer is $\frac{\sqrt{8}}{3}$

$sinA = \frac{1}{3} \Rightarrow$ Since $sin\theta = \frac{opposite}{hypotenuse}$, we have the following right triangle. Then:

$c = \sqrt{3^2 - 1^2} = \sqrt{9 - 1} = \sqrt{8}, cosA = \frac{\sqrt{8}}{3}$

12) The answer is 25π

The equation of a circle in standard form is: $(x - h)^2 + (y - k)^2 = r^2$, where r is the radius of the circle. In this circle the radius is 5. $r^2 = 25 \rightarrow r = 5, (x + 2)^2 + (y - 4)^2 = 25$

Area of a circle: $A = \pi r^2 = \pi(5)^2 = 25\pi$

13) The answer is 5.8×10^5

$580,000 = 5.8 \times 10^5$

14) The answer is 200

The ratio of boy to girls is 2: 3. Therefore, there are 2 boys out of 5 students. To find the answer, first divide the total number of students by 5, then multiply the result by 2.

$500 \div 5 = 100 \Rightarrow 100 \times 2 = 200$

15) The answer is 40

First, find the number. Let x be the number. Write the equation and solve for x.

150% of a number is 75, then: $1.5 \times x = 75 \Rightarrow x = 75 \div 1.5 = 50$

80% of 50 is: $0.8 \times 50 = 40$

16) The answer is $\begin{bmatrix} -5 & 3 \\ 4 & -7 \end{bmatrix}$

First, find $2A. A = \begin{bmatrix} -1 & 2 \\ 1 & -2 \end{bmatrix}$ $2A = 2 \times \begin{bmatrix} -1 & 2 \\ 1 & -2 \end{bmatrix} = \begin{bmatrix} -2 & 4 \\ 2 & -4 \end{bmatrix}$, Now, solve for $2A -$
$B. 2A - B = \begin{bmatrix} -2 & 4 \\ 2 & -4 \end{bmatrix} - \begin{bmatrix} 3 & 1 \\ -2 & 3 \end{bmatrix} = \begin{bmatrix} -2 - 3 & 4 - 1 \\ 2 - (-2) & -4 - 3 \end{bmatrix} = \begin{bmatrix} -5 & 3 \\ 4 & -7 \end{bmatrix}$

17) The answer is $x \geq 6 \cup x \leq -2$
$x - 2 \geq 4 \rightarrow x \geq 4 + 2 \rightarrow x \geq 6$, Or $x - 2 \leq -4 \rightarrow x \leq -4 + 2 \rightarrow x \leq -2$

Then, solution is: $x \geq 6 \cup x \leq -2$

18) The answer is $\frac{8}{17}$

$\tan = \frac{opposite}{adjacent}$, and $\tan x = \frac{8}{15}$, therefore, the opposite side of the angle x is 8 and the adjacent side is 15. Let's draw the triangle.

Using Pythagorean theorem, we have:

$a^2 + b^2 = c^2 \rightarrow 8^2 + 15^2 = c^2 \rightarrow 64 + 225 = c^2 \rightarrow c = 17$, $\sin x = \frac{opposite}{hypotenuse} = \frac{8}{17}$

19) The answer is $x^{\frac{21}{4}}$

$(x^6)^{\frac{7}{8}} = x^{6 \times \frac{7}{8}} = x^{\frac{42}{8}} = x^{\frac{21}{4}}$

20) The answer are $0, -2, -3$

Frist factor the function: $f(x) = x^3 + 5x^2 + 6x = x(x + 2)(x + 3)$, To find the zeros, $f(x)$ should be zero. $f(x) = x(x + 2)(x + 3) = 0$, Therefore, the zeros are: $x = 0$, $(x + 2) = 0 \Rightarrow x = -2$,

$(x + 3) = 0 \Rightarrow x = -3$

21) The answer is 2

$\sin^2 a + \cos^2 a = 1$, then: $x + 1 = 3$, $x = 2$

22) The answer is $\frac{y}{5}$

Solve for x. $\sqrt{5x} = \sqrt{y}$.   Square both sides of the equation: $(\sqrt{5x})^2 = (\sqrt{y})^2$ $5x = y$

$x = \frac{y}{5}$

23) The answer is 59.48

$average = \frac{sum\ of\ terms}{number\ of\ terms}$, The sum of the weight of all girls is: $18 \times 55 = 990\ kg$

The sum of the weight of all boys is: $32 \times 62 = 1,984\ kg$, The sum of the weight of all students is: $990 + 1,984 = 2,974\ kg$. $average = \frac{2,974}{50} = 59.48$

24) The answer is 46

Plug in the value of x and y. $x = 3$ and $y = -3$

$5(x - 2y) + (2 - x)^2 = 5(3 - 2(-3)) + (2 - 3)^2 = 5(3 + 6) + (-1)^2 = 45 + 1 = 46$

25) The answer is 16%

The question is this: 530.40 is what percent of 631? Use percent formula: $part = \frac{percent}{100} \times whole$. $530.40 = \frac{percent}{100} \times 631 \Rightarrow 530.40 = \frac{percent \times 631}{100} \Rightarrow 53,040 = percent \times 631 \Rightarrow percent = \frac{53,040}{631} = 84$. 530.40 is 84% of 631. Therefore, the discount is: $100\% - 84\% = 16\%$

26) The answer is $\frac{1}{2}$

The relationship among all sides of right triangle $30° - 60° - 90°$ is provided in the following triangle: Sine of $30°$ equals to: $\frac{opposite}{hypotenuse} = \frac{x}{2x} = \frac{1}{2}$

27) The answer is $\frac{3}{4} + i$

To simplify the fraction, multiply both numerator and denominator by i.

$\frac{4-3i}{-4i} \times \frac{i}{i} = \frac{4i-3i^2}{-4i^2}$, $i^2 - 1$, Then: $\frac{4i-3i^2}{-4i^2} = \frac{4i-3(-1)}{-4(-1)} = \frac{4i+3}{4} = \frac{4i}{4} + \frac{3}{4} = \frac{3}{4} + i$

28) The answer is 38

Let x be the smallest number. Then, these are the numbers: $x, x + 1, x + 2, x + 3, x + 4$

$average = \frac{sum\ of\ terms}{number\ of\ terms} \Rightarrow 40 = \frac{x+(x+1)+(x+2)+(x+3)+(x+4)}{5} \Rightarrow 40 = \frac{5x+10}{5} \Rightarrow$

$200 = 5x + 10 \Rightarrow 190 = 5x \Rightarrow x = 38$

29) The answer is $-\frac{1}{2}$

The equation of a line in slope intercept form is: $y = mx + b$, Solve for y. $4x - 2y = 14 \Rightarrow -2y = 14 - 4x \Rightarrow y = (14 - 4x) \div (-2) \Rightarrow y = 2x - 7$, The slope is 2. The slope of the line perpendicular to this line is: $m_1 \times m_2 = -1 \Rightarrow 2 \times m_2 = -1 \Rightarrow m_2 = -\frac{1}{2}$

30) The answer is $\frac{2}{x^3} + 4$

$f\big(g(x)\big) = 2 \times (\frac{1}{x})^3 + 4 = \frac{2}{x^3} + 4$

ALEKS Mathematics Practice Test 3

1) The answer is 18

The area of the floor is: $6\ cm \times 24\ cm = 144\ cm^2$. The number is tiles needed $= 144 \div 8 = 18$

2) The answer is 32

The diagonal of the square is 8. Let x be the side.

Use Pythagorean Theorem: $a^2 + b^2 = c^2$

$x^2 + x^2 = 8^2 \Rightarrow 2x^2 = 8^2 \Rightarrow 2x^2 = 64 \Rightarrow x^2 = 32 \Rightarrow x = \sqrt{32}$

The area of the square is: $\sqrt{32} \times \sqrt{32} = 32$

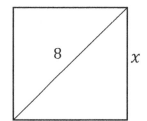

3) The answer is 145

$x = 20 + 125 = 145$

4) The answer is 5

Solve the system of equations by elimination method.

$3x - 4y = -20$
$-x + 2y = 10$ Multiply the second equation by 3, then add it to the first equation.

$\begin{matrix} 3x - 4y = -20 \\ 3(-x + 2y = 10) \end{matrix} \Rightarrow \begin{matrix} 3x - 4y = -20 \\ -3x + 6y = 30 \end{matrix} \Rightarrow$ add the equations $2y = 10 \Rightarrow y = 5$

5) The answer is 8.4 hours

Use distance formula: $Distance = Rate \times time \Rightarrow 420 = 50 \times T$, divide both sides by

50. $420 \div 50 = T \Rightarrow T = 8.4\ hours$. Change hours to minutes for the decimal part. $0.4\ hours = 0.4 \times 60 = 24\ minutes$.

6) The answer is 96

40% of 60 equals to: $0.40 \times 60 = 24$, 12% of 600 equals to: $0.12 \times 600 = 72$

40% of 60 is added to 12% of 600: $24 + 72 = 96$

7) The answer is $7 \le x \le 13$

$|x - 10| \le 3 \to -3 \le x - 10 \le 3 \to -3 + 10 \le x - 10 + 10 \le 3 + 10 \to 7 \le x \le 13$

8) The answer is 40

The area of ΔBED is 16, then: $\frac{4 \times AB}{2} = 16 \to 4 \times AB = 32 \to AB = 8$

The area of ΔBDF is 18, then: $\frac{3 \times BC}{2} = 18 \rightarrow 3 \times BC = 36 \rightarrow BC = 12$

The perimeter of the rectangle is = $2 \times (8 + 12) = 40$

9) The answer is 36 ft

Write a proportion and solve for x. $\frac{3}{2} = \frac{x}{24} \Rightarrow 2x = 3 \times 24 \Rightarrow x = 36 \, ft$

10) The answer is 60 ft

The relationship among all sides of special right triangle

$30° - 60° - 90°$ is provided in this triangle:

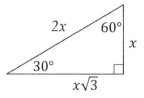

In this triangle, the opposite side of $30°$ angle is half of the hypotenuse.

Draw the shape of this question:

The latter is the hypotenuse. Therefore, the latter is 60 ft.

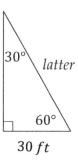

11) The answer is $y^5 + 2x^3 + 7z^3 + x^2 - 2y^2$

$2x^2 + 3y^5 - x^2 + 2z^3 - 2y^2 + 2x^3 - 2y^5 + 5z^3$
$$= 2x^2 - x^2 + 2x^3 - 2y^2 + 3y^5 - 2y^5 + 2z^3 + 5z^3$$
$$= x^2 + 2x^3 - 2y^2 + y^5 + 7z^3$$

Write the expression in standard form:

$x^2 + 2x^3 - 2y^2 + y^5 + 7z^3 = y^5 + 2x^3 + 7z^3 + x^2 - 2y^2$

12) The answer is 475

Add the first 5 numbers. $40 + 45 + 50 + 35 + 55 = 225$

To find the distance traveled in the next 5 hours, multiply the average by number of hours.

$Distance = Average \times Rate = 50 \times 5 = 250.$ Add both numbers. $250 + 225 = 475$

13) The answer is $4\sqrt{3}$

Based on triangle similarity theorem: $\frac{a}{a+b} = \frac{c}{3} \rightarrow c = \frac{3a}{a+b} = \frac{3\sqrt{3}}{3\sqrt{3}} = 1 \rightarrow$ area of shaded region is:

$\left(\frac{c+3}{2}\right)(b) = \frac{4}{2} \times 2\sqrt{3} = 4\sqrt{3}$

14) The answer is $80cm$

$One \ liter = 1,000 \ cm^3 \rightarrow 6 \ liters = 6,000 \ cm^3$ $6,000 = 15 \times 5 \times h \rightarrow h = \frac{6,000}{75} = 80cm$

15) The answer is 60

$$\frac{2}{3} \times 90 = 60$$

16) The answer is $600 \: ml$

4% of the volume of the solution is alcohol. Let x be the volume of the solution.

Then: $4\% \: of \: x = 24 \: ml \Rightarrow 0.04 \: x = 24 \Rightarrow x = 24 \div 0.04 = 600$

17) The answer is 4

Solve for x. $\frac{3x}{16} = \frac{x-1}{4}$. Multiply the second fraction by 4. $\frac{3x}{16} = \frac{4(x-1)}{4 \times 4}$. Tow denominators are equal. Therefore, the numerators must be equal. $3x = 4x - 4, \quad 0 = x - 4 , 4 = x$

18) The answer is $-60 + 2i$

We know that: $i = \sqrt{-1} \Rightarrow i^2 = -1$

$(-5 + 9i)(3 + 5i) = -15 - 25i + 27i + 45i^2 = -15 + 2i - 45 = -60 + 2i$

19) The answer is $\frac{3}{5}$

$sin\theta = \frac{4}{5} \Rightarrow$ we have following triangle, then

$c = \sqrt{5^2 - 4^2} = \sqrt{25 - 16} = \sqrt{9} = 3, cos\theta = \frac{3}{5}$

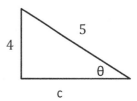

20) The answer is 225

$0.6x = (0.3) \times 20 \rightarrow x = 10 \rightarrow (x + 5)^2 = (15)^2 = 225$

21) The answer is $50 \: miles$

Use the information provided in the question to draw the shape.

Use Pythagorean Theorem: $a^2 + b^2 = c^2$

$40^2 + 30^{\: 2} = c^2 \Rightarrow 1,600 + 900 = c^2 \Rightarrow 2,500 = c^2 \Rightarrow c = 50$

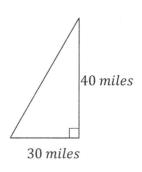

22) The answer is $\frac{10}{3}$

<u>METHOD ONE</u>

$log_4(x + 2) - log_4(x - 2) = 1$, Add $log_4(x - 2)$ to both sides

$log_4(x + 2) - log_4(x - 2) + log_4(x - 2) = 1 + log_4(x - 2)$

$log_4(x + 2) = 1 + log_4(x - 2)$

Apply logarithm rule: $a = log_b(b^a) \Rightarrow 1 = log_4(4^1) = log_4(4)$

then: $log_4(x + 2) = log_4(4) + log_4(x - 2)$

Logarithm rule: $log_c(a) + log_c(b) = log_c(ab)$

then: $log_4(4) + log_4(x - 2) = log_4(4(x - 2))$

$\log_4(x + 2) = \log_4(4(x - 2))$

When the logs have the same base: $log_b(f(x)) = log_b(g(x)) = f(x) = g(x)$

$(x + 2) = 4(x - 2), x = \dfrac{10}{3}$

<u>METHOD TWO</u>

We know that: $\quad log_a b - log_a c = log_a \dfrac{b}{c} \quad$ and $\quad log_a b = c \Rightarrow b = a^c$

Then: $log_4(x + 2) - log_4(x - 2) = log_4 \dfrac{x+2}{x-2} = 1 \Rightarrow \dfrac{x+2}{x-2} = 4^1 = 4 \Rightarrow x + 2 = 4(x - 2)$

$\Rightarrow x + 2 = 4x - 8 \Rightarrow 4x - x = 8 + 2 \rightarrow 3x = 10 \Rightarrow x = \dfrac{10}{3}$

23) The answer is $\dfrac{2}{5}$

Set of number that are not composite between 1 and 25: $A = \{1, 2, 3, 5, 7, 11, 13, 17, 19, 23\}$

$Probability = \dfrac{number\ of\ desired\ outcomes}{number\ of\ total\ outcomes} = \dfrac{10}{25} = \dfrac{2}{5}$

24) The answer is 3.9

$sine\ \theta = \dfrac{opposite}{hypotenuse}.\ sine\ 40° = \dfrac{AC}{6} \rightarrow 6 \times sine\ 40° = AC,$

now use a calculator to find $sine\ 40°.\ sine\ 40° \cong 0.642 \rightarrow AC \cong 3.9$

25) The answer is 105

$y = 4ab + 3b^3$. Plug in the values of a and b in the equation: $a = 2$ and $b = 3$

$y = 4(2)(3) + 3(3)^3 = 24 + 3(27) = 24 + 81 = 105$

26) The answer is $-x^2 - 3x - 6$

$(g - f)(x) = g(x) - f(x) = (-x^2 - 1 - 2x) - (5 + x)$

$- x^2 - 1 - 2x - 5 - x = -x^2 - 3x - 6$

27) The answer is 1

$tangent\ β = \dfrac{1}{cotangent\ β} = \dfrac{1}{1} = 1$

28) The answer is $(-10, 3)$

When points are reflected over y-axis, the value of y in the coordinates doesn't change and the sign of x changes. Therefore, the coordinates of point B is $(-10, 3)$.

29) The answer is 60

Perimeter of figure A is: $2\pi r = 2\pi\frac{20}{2} = 20\pi = 20 \times 3 = 60$

Area of figure B is: $5 \times 12 = 60$, $Average = \frac{60+60}{2} = \frac{120}{2} = 60$

30) The answer is 0

$g(x) = -2$, then $f\big(g(x)\big) = f(-2) = 2(-2)^3 + 5(-2)^2 + 2(-2) = -16 + 20 - 4 = 0$

ALEKS Mathematics Practice Test 4

1) The answer is $\frac{3x-1}{x^2-x}$

$$\left(\frac{f}{g}\right)(x) = \frac{f(x)}{g(x)} = \frac{3x-1}{x^2-x}$$

2) The answer is 840

Use simple interest formula: $I = prt$ (I = interest, p = principal, r = rate, t = time)

$$I = (12,000)(0.035)(2) = 840$$

3) The answer is 10,000

Number of visiting fans: $\frac{2\times 25,000}{5} = 10,000$

4) The answer is 144°

The sum of all angles in a quadrilateral is 360 degrees. Let x be the smallest angle in the quadrilateral. Then the angles are: $x, 2x, 3x, 4x, x + 2x + 3x + 4x = 360 \rightarrow 10x = 360 \rightarrow x = 36$, The angles in the quadrilateral are: $36°, 72°, 108°,$ and $144°$

5) The answer is $\frac{8\sqrt{\pi}}{\pi}$

Formula for the area of a circle is: $A = \pi r^2$, Using 64 for the area of the circle we have: $64 = \pi r^2$. Let's solve for the radius (r). $\frac{64}{\pi} = r^2 \rightarrow r = \sqrt{\frac{64}{\pi}} = \frac{8}{\sqrt{\pi}} = \frac{8}{\sqrt{\pi}} \times \frac{\sqrt{\pi}}{\sqrt{\pi}} = \frac{8\sqrt{\pi}}{\pi}$

6) The answer is 72
Length of the rectangle is: $\frac{5}{4} \times 16 = 20$, perimeter of rectangle is: $2 \times (20 + 16) = 72$
7) The answer is 145°

The angle x and 35 are complementary angles. Therefore: $x + 35 = 180 \rightarrow$

$$x = 180° - 35° = 145°$$

8) The answer is 30
The sum of supplement angles is 180. Let x be that angle. Therefore, $x + 5x = 180$
$6x = 180$, divide both sides by 6: $x = 30$
9) The answer is -2

Solving Systems of Equations by Elimination: Multiply the first equation by (-2), then add it to the second equation.

$$\begin{array}{l} -2(2x + 5y = 11) \\ \underline{4x - 2y = -14} \end{array} \Rightarrow \begin{array}{l} -4x - 10y = -22 \\ \underline{4x - 2y = -14} \end{array} \Rightarrow -12y = -36 \Rightarrow y = 3$$

Plug in the value of y into one of the equations and solve for x.

$$2x + 5(3) = 11 \Rightarrow 2x + 15 = 11 \Rightarrow 2x = -4 \Rightarrow x = -2$$

10) The answer is $60,000$

Three times of 24,000 is 72,000. One sixth of them cancelled their tickets. One sixth of 72,000 equals $12,000$ ($\frac{1}{6} \times 72,000 = 12,000$). $60,000$ ($72,000 - 12,000 = 60,000$) fans are attending this week.

11) The answer is $\frac{\sqrt{15}}{4}$

$sinA = \frac{1}{4} \Rightarrow$ Since $sin\theta = \frac{opposite}{hypotenuse}$, we have the following right triangle. Then:

$$c = \sqrt{4^2 - 1^2} = \sqrt{16 - 1} = \sqrt{15}, cosA = \frac{\sqrt{15}}{4}$$

12) The answer is 16π

The equation of a circle in standard form is: $(x - h)^2 + (y - k)^2 = r^2$, where r is the radius of the circle. In this circle the radius is 4. $r^2 = 16 \rightarrow r = 4$, $(x + 2)^2 + (y - 4)^2 = 16$, Area of a circle: $A = \pi r^2 = \pi(4)^2 = 16\pi$

13) The answer is 6.7×10^5

$$670,000 = 6.7 \times 10^5$$

14) The answer is 240

The ratio of boy to girls is $2:3$. Therefore, there are 2 boys out of 5 students. To find the answer, first divide the total number of students by 5, then multiply the result by 2.

$$600 \div 5 = 120 \Rightarrow 120 \times 2 = 240$$

15) The answer is 45

First, find the number. Let x be the number. Write the equation and solve for x. 150% of a number is 75, then: $1.5 \times x = 75 \Rightarrow x = 75 \div 1.5 = 50$, 90% of 50 is: $0.9 \times 50 = 45$

16) The answer is $\begin{bmatrix} -6 & 3 \\ 4 & -7 \end{bmatrix}$

First, find $2A$. $A = \begin{bmatrix} -1 & 2 \\ 1 & -2 \end{bmatrix}$ $2A = 2 \times \begin{bmatrix} -1 & 2 \\ 1 & -2 \end{bmatrix} = \begin{bmatrix} -2 & 4 \\ 2 & -4 \end{bmatrix}$

Now, solve for $2A - B$.

$$2A - B = \begin{bmatrix} -2 & 4 \\ 2 & -4 \end{bmatrix} - \begin{bmatrix} 4 & 1 \\ -2 & 3 \end{bmatrix} = \begin{bmatrix} -2 - 4 & 4 - 1 \\ 2 - (-2) & -4 - 3 \end{bmatrix} = \begin{bmatrix} -6 & 3 \\ 4 & -7 \end{bmatrix}$$

17) The answer is $x \geq 5 \cup x \leq -1$

$x - 2 \geq 3 \rightarrow x \geq 3 + 2 \rightarrow x \geq 5$, Or $x - 2 \leq -3 \rightarrow x \leq -3 + 2 \rightarrow x \leq -1$

Then, solution is: $x \geq 5 \cup x \leq -1$

18) The answer is $\frac{8}{17}$

$\tan = \frac{opposite}{adjacent}$, and $\tan x = \frac{8}{15}$, therefore, the opposite side of the angle x is 8 and the adjacent side is 15. Let's draw the triangle.

Using Pythagorean theorem, we have: $a^2 + b^2 = c^2 \rightarrow 8^2 + 15^2 = c^2 \rightarrow 64 + 225 = c^2 \rightarrow$ $c = 17$, $\sin x = \frac{opposite}{hypotenuse} = \frac{8}{17}$

19) The answer is $x^{\frac{15}{4}}$

$(x^6)^{\frac{5}{8}} = x^{6 \times \frac{5}{8}} = x^{\frac{30}{8}} = x^{\frac{15}{4}}$

20) The answer are $0, -2, -3$

Frist factor the function: $f(x) = x^3 + 6x^2 + 8x = x\,(x+4)(x+2)$, To find the zeros, $f(x)$ should be zero. $f(x) = x\,(x+4)(x+2) = 0$, Therefore, the zeros are: $x = 0$, $(x+4) = 0 \Rightarrow x = -4$, $(x+2) = 0 \Rightarrow x = -2$

21) The answer is 2

$\sin^2 a + \cos^2 a = 1$, then: $x + 1 = 3$, $x = 2$

22) The answer is $\frac{y}{6}$

Solve for x. $\sqrt{6x} = \sqrt{y}$.   Square both sides of the equation:

$(\sqrt{6x})^2 = (\sqrt{y})^2$ $6x = y$ $x = \frac{y}{6}$

23) The answer is 61.28

$average = \frac{sum\ of\ terms}{number\ of\ terms}$, The sum of the weight of all girls is: $18 \times 60 = 1,080\ kg$

The sum of the weight of all boys is: $32 \times 62 = 1,984\ kg$, The sum of the weight of all students is: $1,080 + 1,984 = 3,064\ kg$. $average = \frac{3,064}{50} = 61.28$

24) The answer is 36

Plug in the value of x and y. $x = 3$ and $y = -2$

$5(x - 2y) + (2 - x)^2 = 5(3 - 2(-2)) + (2 - 3)^2 = 5(3 + 4) + (-1)^2 = 35 + 1 = 36$

25) The answer is 15%

The question is this: 530.40 is what percent of 624?

Use percent formula: $part = \frac{percent}{100} \times whole$

$530.40 = \frac{percent}{100} \times 624 \Rightarrow 530.40 = \frac{percent \times 624}{100} \Rightarrow 53,040 = percent \times 624 \Rightarrow$

$percent = \frac{53,040}{624} = 85.$ 530.40 is 85% of 624. Therefore, the discount is: $100\% - 85\% = 15\%$

26) The answer is $\frac{1}{2}$

The relationship among all sides of right triangle $30° - 60° - 90°$ is provided in the following triangle:

Sine of $30°$ equals to: $\frac{opposite}{hypotenuse} = \frac{x}{2x} = \frac{1}{2}$

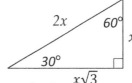

27) The answer is $\frac{3}{5} + i$

To simplify the fraction, multiply both numerator and denominator by i.

$\frac{5-3i}{-5i} \times \frac{i}{i} = \frac{5i-3i^2}{-5i^2}, i^2 - 1,$ Then: $\frac{5i-3i^2}{-5i^2} = \frac{5i-3(-1)}{-5(-1)} = \frac{5i+3}{5} = \frac{5i}{5} + \frac{3}{5} = \frac{3}{5} + i$

28) The answer is 36

Let x be the smallest number. Then, these are the numbers: $x, x + 1, x + 2, x + 3, x + 4$

$average = \frac{sum\ of\ terms}{number\ of\ terms} \Rightarrow 38 = \frac{x+(x+1)+(x+2)+(x+3)+(x+4)}{5} \Rightarrow 38 = \frac{5x+10}{5} \Rightarrow$

$190 = 5x + 10 \Rightarrow 180 = 5x \Rightarrow x = 36$

29) The answer is $-\frac{1}{2}$

The equation of a line in slope intercept form is: $y = mx + b$. Solve for y. $4x - 2y = 12 \Rightarrow -2y = 12 - 4x \Rightarrow y = (12 - 4x) \div (-2) \Rightarrow y = 2x - 6$

The slope is 2. The slope of the line perpendicular to this line is:

$m_1 \times m_2 = -1 \Rightarrow 2 \times m_2 = -1 \Rightarrow m_2 = -\frac{1}{2}$

30) The answer is $\frac{2}{x^4} + 2$

$f(g(x)) = 2 \times (\frac{1}{x})^4 + 2 = \frac{2}{x^4} + 2$

ALEKS Mathematics Practice Test 5

1) The answer is $x^3 + 21x - 20$

Use FOIL (First, Out, In, Last), $(x - 5)(x^2 + 5x + 4) = x^3 + 5x^2 + 4x - 5x^2 - 25x - 20 = x^3 + 21x - 20$

2) The answer is -38

Use PEMDAS (order of operation): $5 + 8 \times (-3) - [4 + 22 \times 5] \div 6 = 5 + 8 \times (-3) - [4 + 110] \div 6 = 5 + 8 \times (-3) - [114] \div 6 = 5 + (-24) - 19 = 5 + (-24) - 19 = 5 - 43 = -38$

3) The answer is $\dfrac{-x - 3}{2x^2 - 10}$

Simplify: $\dfrac{\frac{1}{2} - \frac{x+5}{4}}{\frac{x^2}{2} - \frac{5}{2}} = \dfrac{\frac{1}{2} - \frac{x+5}{4}}{\frac{x^2 - 5}{2}} = \dfrac{2(\frac{1}{2} - \frac{x+5}{4})}{x^2 - 5}$ ⇒Simplify: $\dfrac{1}{2} - \dfrac{x+5}{4} = \dfrac{-x-3}{4}$

then: $\dfrac{2(\frac{-x-3}{4})}{x^2 - 5} = \dfrac{\frac{-x-3}{2}}{x^2 - 5} = \dfrac{-x-3}{2(x^2 - 5)} = \dfrac{-x-3}{2x^2 - 10}$

4) The answer is 78

Number of squares equal to: $\dfrac{52 \times 12}{4 \times 2} = 13 \times 6 = 78$

5) The answer is $x \leq 5$

Simplify: $5 + 2x \leq 15 \Rightarrow 2x \leq 15 - 5 \Rightarrow 2x \leq 10 \Rightarrow x \leq 5$

6) The answer is $635

$55 \times \$66 = \$3,630$ Payable amount is: $\$4,265 - \$3,630 = \$635$

7) The answer is $x^{\frac{5}{2}}$

$(x^4)^{\frac{5}{8}} = x^{4 \times \frac{5}{8}} = x^{\frac{20}{8}} = x^{\frac{5}{2}}$

8) The answer is 5231.6

Underline the tenth place: $2531.\underline{5}8245$, Look to the right if it is 5 or bigger, add 1 to the underlined digit. Then, round up the decimal to 5231.6

9) The answer is 60

$25 \times \dfrac{x}{100} = 15$ $\Rightarrow$ $25 \times x = 1,500$ $\Rightarrow$ $x = \dfrac{1,500}{25} = 60$

10) The answer is $9.48

$\$44 - \$34.52 = \$9.48$

11) The answer is $45°$

$90° + 45° = 135° \rightarrow 180° - 135° = 45°$

12) The answer is $(x - 4)(x - 3)$

$x^2 - 7x + 12 = (x - 4)(x - 3)$

13) The answer is $60 ft$

The relationship among all sides of special right triangle

$30° - 60° - 90°$ is provided in this triangle:

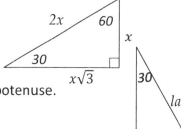

In this triangle, the opposite side of $30°$ angle is half of the hypotenuse.

Draw the shape of this question:

The latter is the hypotenuse. Therefore, the latter is $60\ ft$.

14) The answer is 5

$C = \sqrt{(x_A - x_B)^2 + (y - y_B)^2}$, $C = \sqrt{(1 - (-2))^2 + (3 - 7)^2} \rightarrow C = \sqrt{(3)^2 + (-4)^2} \rightarrow$
$C = \sqrt{9 + 16} \rightarrow C = \sqrt{25} = 5$

15) The answer is 0.0142

$\frac{2}{140} = \frac{1}{70} = 0.0142857143 \cong 0.0142$

16) The answer is 12

$\frac{a + b}{2} = 9 \qquad \Rightarrow \qquad a + b = 18, \frac{a + b + c}{3} = 10 \qquad \Rightarrow \qquad a + b + c = 30$

$18 + c = 30 \quad \Rightarrow \quad c = 30 - 18 = 12$

17) The answer is $-\frac{1}{2}, -3$

$x_{1,2} = \frac{-b \pm \sqrt{b^2 - 4ac}}{2a}$, $ax^2 + bx + c = 0 \Rightarrow 4x^2 + 14x + 6 = 0 \qquad \Rightarrow$ then: $a = 4, b = 14$ and $c = 6$

$x = \frac{-14 + \sqrt{14^2 - 4 \times 4 \times 6}}{2 \times 4} = -\frac{1}{2}$, $x = \frac{-14 - \sqrt{14^2 - 4 \times 4 \times 6}}{2 \times 4} = -3$

18) The answer is 13

$7^5 \times 7^8 = 7^{5+8} = 7^{13} = 7^x \rightarrow x = 13$

19) The answer is 33

$33 + 36 + 30 = 99$, $Average = \frac{99}{3} = 33$

20) The answer is $-1 + \sqrt{6}, -1 - \sqrt{6}$

$x_{1,2} = \frac{-b \pm \sqrt{b^2 - 4ac}}{2a}$, $ax^2 + bx + c = 0, x^2 + 2x - 5 = 0 \qquad \Rightarrow \qquad$ then: $a = 1, b = 2$
and $c = -5$

$$x = \frac{-2 + \sqrt{2^2 - 4 \times 1 \times (-5)}}{2 \times 1} = -1 + \sqrt{6}, x = \frac{-2 - \sqrt{2^2 - 4 \times 1 \times (-5)}}{2 \times 1} = -1 - \sqrt{6}$$

21) The answer is $(3, 3)$

$$\begin{cases} -2x - y = -9 \\ 5x - 2y = 9 \end{cases} \Rightarrow \text{Multiplication } (-2) \text{ in first equation} \Rightarrow \begin{cases} 4x + 2y = 18 \\ 5x - 2y = 9 \end{cases}$$

Add two equations together $\Rightarrow 9x = 27 \Rightarrow x = 3$ then: $y = 3$

22) The answer is 6

$|9 - (12 \div |2 - 6|)| = |9 - (12 \div |-4|)| = |9 - (12 \div 4)| = |9 - 3| = |6| = 6$

23) The answer is 32

$$\log_2 x = 5$$

Apply logarithm rule: $= \log_b(b^a)$, $5 = \log_2(2^5) = \log_2(32)$

$\log_2 x = \log_2(32)$, When the logs have the same base:

$\log_b(f(x)) = \log_b(g(x)) \Rightarrow f(x) = g(x)$, then: $x = 32$

24) The answer is $\frac{14}{x^3}$

$\frac{x^3}{14} \Rightarrow$ reciprocal is : $\frac{14}{x^3}$

25) The answer is 60

Plug in 140 for F and then solve for C.

$$C = \frac{5}{9}(F - 32) \Rightarrow C = \frac{5}{9}(140 - 32) \Rightarrow C = \frac{5}{9}(108) = 60$$

26) The answer is $12i - 54$

We know that: $i = \sqrt{-1} \Rightarrow i^2 = -1$

$(-3 + 9i)(3 + 5i) = -9 - 15i + 27i + 45i^2 = -9 + 12i - 45 = 12i - 54$

27) The answer is $-\sqrt{3}$

$$\tan \frac{2\pi}{3} = \frac{\sin\frac{2\pi}{3}}{\cos\frac{2\pi}{3}} = \frac{\frac{\sqrt{3}}{2}}{-\frac{1}{2}} = -\sqrt{3}$$

28) The answer is $\frac{5x - 1}{x^2 - x}$

$(\frac{f}{g})(x) = \frac{f(x)}{g(x)} = \frac{5x - 1}{x^2 - x}$

29) The answer is $(4, -9)$, $\sqrt{3}$

$(x - h)^2 + (y - k)^2 = r^2 \Rightarrow$ center: (h, k) and radius: r

$(x - 4)^2 + (y + 7)^2 = 3 \Rightarrow$ center: $(4, -9)$ and radius: $\sqrt{3}$

30) The answer is $(x + 4)^2 + (y - 2)^2 = 1$

Use formula of a circle in the coordinate plane: $(x - h)^2 + (y - k)^2 = r^2 \Rightarrow$ center: (h, k) and radius: r, center: $(-4, 2) \quad \Rightarrow h = -4, k = 2$

circumference $= 2\pi \Rightarrow$ circumference $= 2\pi r = 2\pi \qquad \Rightarrow \qquad r = 1$

$(x + 4)^2 + (y - 2)^2 = 1$

"Effortless Math" Publications

Effortless Math authors' team strives to prepare and publish the best quality Mathematics learning resources to make learning Math easier for all. We hope that our publications help you or your student Math in an effective way.

We all in Effortless Math wish you good luck and successful studies!

Effortless Math Authors

www.EffortlessMath.com

... So Much More Online!

✓ FREE Math lessons

✓ More Math learning books!

✓ Mathematics Worksheets

✓ Online Math Tutors

Need a PDF version of this book?

Visit www.EffortlessMath.com

Made in the USA
Coppell, TX
31 May 2020

26753206R00050